Based on the episode from the animated TV series
produced by Scholastic Productions, Inc.
Based on *The Magic School Bus* book series
written by Joanna Cole and illustrated by Bruce Degen

TV tie-in book by Pat Relf and illustrated by Carolyn Bracken.
TV script written by George Arthur Bloom.

Scholastic Children's Books,
Commonwealth House, 1-19 New Oxford Street,
London WC1A 1NU, UK
a division of Scholastic Ltd

London ~ New York ~ Toronto ~ Sydney ~ Auckland

First published by Scholastic Inc. 1996
This edition published in the UK by Scholastic Ltd 1997

ISBN 0 590 19351 1

Printed in Italy by Amadeus S.p.A.- Rome

We're always doing something interesting – and fun – in Miss Frizzle's class. The other day we were learning about water. All of us were doing projects.

Wanda and Arnold made a model waterworks. "Now, just add water!" said Wanda.

Wanda took Arnold into the girls' bathroom to get water. "Hurry, Wanda," said Arnold. "This is embarrassing! What if somebody catches me in here?"

Wanda laughed. "Who's going to catch us – Tiffany?"

Arnold turned red.

At last the bucket was full.

"Okay, Arnold, you can take out the plug and turn off the water now," said Wanda. She picked up the heavy bucket and headed back to the classroom.

Arnold started to turn off the water. Just then he heard someone come in. It was Tiffany!

Tiffany ran. Arnold chased after her. He had to explain! But he'd forgotten to turn off the tap. The water kept dripping...

Arnold didn't get very far. Tim came into the corridor.

"It's time for your report," he said.

Arnold shook his head. So far, he was having a terrible day!

In the classroom, Wanda was trying out their waterworks model. "We pour in the water," said Wanda. "It runs through the cleaning tanks, and out of the pipe at the other end. Perfect!"

When Carlos opened the mop cupboard, a big wave of water came out. And out of the water stepped our teacher, Miss Frizzle. Did I mention that Miss Frizzle is ... well ... a little different?

"Good morning, class!" she said. "Are you ready to learn about water?"

"I'd rather go on the Surf Ride at Waterland," said Wanda. Miss Frizzle got that funny look she sometimes gets. "Of course!" she exclaimed. "To learn about water, we really need to get *into* it. Time for a field trip!"

The Friz led us outside to the old school bus.

Dorothy Ann stopped to check her rain gauge. "Wow, it really rained a lot!" she said.

"Nearly five centimetres this morning," said Tim.

Dorothy Ann wrote the information in her notebook. "That's a school record!"

"All aboard!" called the Friz from the bus.

"Here we go!" said the Friz.

All of a sudden, there was a loud gurgling noise.

Arnold's eyes widened. "I have a feeling this isn't the way to Waterland," he said.

"Who said we were going to Waterland?" said Miss Frizzle. "Why *visit* the water when we can actually be water? Hold on!"

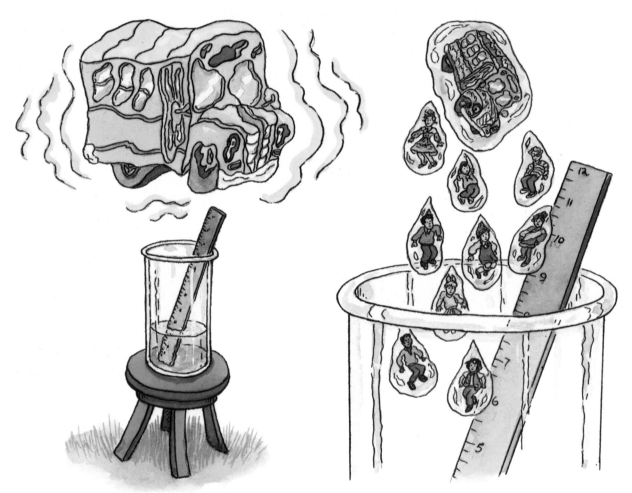

Suddenly the whole bus rose into the air. We felt cool and heavy. We were turning into water! With a big *plop*, we dripped right into Dorothy Ann's rain gauge.

"Welcome to the *real* Waterland," said Miss Frizzle.

Wanda floated happily inside the rain gauge. "This is great!" she exclaimed. "It's nice and warm in here with the sun shining down. Can we stay all day?"

"I don't think so," said Ralphie, who was starting to float up into the air. "I think we're going uuuuuup!"

Miss Frizzle nodded as she floated up, too. "When water is warmed by the sun, it evaporates or turns into a gas called water vapour," she explained.

Soon we had all turned into water vapour and were rising up into the sky.

"This is too weird," said Arnold. "I wish I could be water again."

"You *are* water, Arnold," said Dorothy Ann. "But right now you are water *vapour*, which is a gas, not a liquid."

It was getting cold way up there in the air.

"Brrr!" said Wanda. "Hey, look! I'm turning back into droplets!"

Miss Frizzle smiled. This field trip was going according to her plan. "Arnold is getting his wish. We're changing back into a liquid. We're condensing!" said the Friz.

It felt tickly to be a cloud, especially when the wind started to blow. It blew us across some water... and over a forest. Then we formed one big cloud.

"Where are we?" asked Arnold.

"On our way down, I believe," answered Miss Frizzle.

And, sure enough, we were starting to drip. Our cloud was raining!

We dropped on to leaves and slid down to the ground.
Then we found each other again and started downhill.
"Go with the flow, class!" said Miss Frizzle happily.

What a ride! We ran downhill to a river, which got bigger and bigger. Suddenly, with a big *whoosh*, we went over a waterfall.

"Where's all this water going in such a hurry?" asked Phoebe when she came to the surface again.

"Water always flows to the lowest spot," answered the Friz. "And there it is. The ocean!"

We made it all the way to the ocean.

"Good!" said Arnold. "Now we can rest."

"Sorry, Arnold," said Miss Frizzle. "This is no time to rest. Don't you feel the sun warming us? What happens next?"

"We . . . evaporate?" said Arnold uncertainly as we all rose into the air.

"Correct!" called the Friz. "And when we reach cold air?" she asked.

"We condense!" said Phoebe happily. "I love this part. We turn into clouds and the wind blows us somewhere."

"AGAIN?!" moaned Arnold.

"This is not the last time, either, Arnold," said Miss Frizzle.

"You mean, water keeps evaporating, condensing, and raining *forever*?" gasped Arnold.

"Bingo!" said the Friz. "That's why it's called the water *cycle*. It happens over and over again. In fact, I think we're about to rain again right now!"

We rained right on to our own school.

"Whew! Back at last!" said Arnold. Then he looked through the window where he and Wanda had landed. "Oh, my gosh! It's the girls' bathroom. I left the plug in and the water was dripping!"

"Liz has it under control," said Wanda. "Or is her tail stuck in the tap?"

Liz nodded frantically as she tried to pull her tail out.

"We've got to help Liz!" Wanda said. "But how can we get into the bathroom?"

Arnold thought hard. "I have an idea!" he said. "We're water. We can get through the bathroom pipes. But to get to the pipes we have to start at the waterworks – the *real* waterworks. Follow me!"

Arnold found a sunny spot. Right away, he evaporated.

Here we go again!

What could we do? We all followed Arnold. It wasn't far to the waterworks, and fortunately the wind was blowing in the right direction.

"Here we are!" announced Arnold. "We're right over the reservoir."

Wanda was excited. "Hey, this is where the water is stored and where the waterworks begin."

"Squeeze together, class!" said Miss Frizzle. "Prepare to rain!"

We felt ourselves being sucked into a big pipe with a lot of dirt and gunk from the reservoir.

"I can't believe we drink this stuff!" said Carlos.

"It gets . . . I mean, *we* get cleaned first," said Arnold. "Here come the strainers!"

We passed through what looked like a wire fence, leaving a lot of the gunk behind. Then we floated through some white, puffy stuff.

"It's alum," explained Arnold. "It sponges up dirt. Now on to the settling basin!"

The alum and dirt fell to the bottom of the settling basin. A lot cleaner, we floated on.

"Last stop, filtration tank!" announced Arnold as we flowed through some scratchy gravel. "Now we just have to find the right pipe to take us back to school."

"This way!" Arnold said, and we all followed. The pipes were big at first, but they got smaller and smaller as we went along underneath the town.

"How much further to the school and the girls' bathroom?" asked Wanda.

"This must be it," Arnold said.

"Hey, it's Liz's tail," said Wanda. She pushed it. She pushed harder. We all pushed. It didn't budge. Liz's tail really was stuck.

"Well, I hate to do this, but it has to be done," said Wanda. And she bit Liz's tail – hard!

Now that the tap was open, we all flooded into the bathroom sink ... over the edge ... and on to the floor.

"Oh, no!" groaned Arnold. "Here comes Tiffany again! Don't let her see me!"

But all Tiffany saw was a flood in progress. "Holy cow!" she yelled, and she ran to turn off the tap. By that time, we had all flowed out of the open door, down the hall, and out into the school yard.

"Perfect!" said the Friz. "Now there's enough room for us – and the bus – to return to normal size. All aboard, please, class!"

We all flowed into the bus. With a turn of Miss Frizzle's key and a big swooshing sound, we grew to normal size.

"Tiffany!" called Arnold, running to help her up from a puddle of water. "Are you all right?"

"I think so," she answered. "Thank you, Arnold."

Arnold's face turned pink, but he was grinning from ear to ear.

"Well, class, what did you think of the water cycle?" asked Miss Frizzle as we followed her into school.

Wanda smiled. "As usual, Miss Frizzle," she said, "your field trip really made a *splash*!"

Dear Magic School Bus Books,

Come on! You can't fool me.

First of all, kids can't turn into water.

Second, I know that water collects, evaporates, condenses, and rains, but it probably wouldn't happen three times in one day to one drop of water. Sometimes the water cycle takes weeks or years—or thousands of years, if it is frozen in a glacier or something.

And chomping on a lizard's tail is dangerous—to the lizard and the chomper. What do you say to that?

Signed,
You Can't Fool Me

Dear Can't Fool,

Okay, kids can't turn into water. We just wanted them to *behave* like water. Please don't rain on our parade!

True, the water cycle can take a long time. But when you're with Miss Frizzle, things tend to happen fast.

And about the chomp: Liz and Wanda turned out fine, but you're right.

Don't try that at home.

Yours truly,
The Editor

A Note to Kids, Teachers and Parents

You've just taken a trip through the water cycle. It could have gone on much longer - forever, in fact, because the water cycle never ends. The Earth constantly moves water around on its surface. Water travels downhill in rivers to oceans, the lowest places on the Earth's surface; heat from the sun changes surface water to a gas; when the vapour cools, it condenses and falls to Earth again as rain or snow; and, back on Earth, it starts to collect again, travelling downhill in rivulets and rivers to the ocean. The cycle is complete.

Along the way, plants, animals and humans take water from the cycle, use it, and return it, one way or another, to the cycle. Humans take water for drinking, cooking, cleaning and manufacturing and they return it to the water cycle.

Although there is lots of water in the world, it is not always where we want it when we want it. Only a tiny part of the Earth's water is drinkable. Our drinkable water is a precious resource. We need to borrow it only as we need it, and to return it to the water cycle in the best condition we can.

Miss Frizzle